JOKE BOOK

11
YEAR OLD
EDITION

TRY
NOT
TO
LAUGH
CHALLENGE™

Try Not To Laugh Challenge
BONUS PLAY

Join our Joke Club and get the Bonus Play PDF!

Simply send us an email to:

 **TNTLPublishing@gmail.com**

and you will get the following:

- 10 Hilarious, Bonus Jokes
- An entry in our Monthly Giveaway of a $50 Amazon Gift card!

We draw a new winner each month and will contact you via email!

Good luck!

😊

WELCOME TO THE
TRY NOT TO LAUGH CHALLENGE!

RULES OF THE GAME:

★ Grab a friend or family member, a pen/pencil, and your comedic skills! Determine who will be "Jokester 1" and "Jokester 2".

★ Take turns reading the jokes aloud to each other, and check the box next to each joke you get a laugh from! Each laugh box is worth 1 point, and the pages are labeled to instruct and guide when it is each player's turn.

★ Once you have both completed telling jokes in the round, tally up your laugh points and mark it down on each score page! There is a total of 10 Rounds.

★ Play as many rounds as you like! Once you reach the last round, Round 10, tally up ALL points from the previous rounds to determine who is the CHAMPION LAUGH MASTER!

★ Round 11 - The Tie-Breaker Round.

In the event of a tie, proceed to Round 11. This round will be 'Winner Takes All!', so whoever scores more laugh points in this round alone, is crowned the CHAMPION LAUGH MASTER!

TIP: Use an expressive voice, facial expressions, and even silly body movement to really get the most out of each joke and keep the crowd laughing!

Now, it's time to play!

ROUND 1

 **JOKESTER 1**

Why were the sweaters so close?

LAUGH ⬚

They were from a really tight-knit family!

How far do teeth go to reach happiness?

LAUGH ⬚

5miles.

Which rock group is the President's favorite?

LAUGH ⬚

Mount Rushmore.

Why did the bagels forfeit the basketball game?

LAUGH ⬚

They had no center!

What kind of hats do legs wear?

Knee CAPS!

☐ LAUGH

I named my dog 'Gut' because I always trust him.

☐ LAUGH

Why did the wax melt?

It couldn't candle the heat!

☐ LAUGH

What toy is always in the bathroom?

☐ LAUGH

The TOY-let!

Pass the book to Jokester 2! ➝

What did the potato say, before getting skinned?

"This does not a-PEEL to me."

☐ LAUGH

I used to really love burrito jokes, but not anymore. Bean there, pun that. They're just too cheesy!

☐ LAUGH

Did the line cook get in trouble for eating a pickle?

No, turns out it wasn't a big DILL!

☐ LAUGH

What do you call it when the butcher gives you the wrong order?

A mis-STEAK.

☐ LAUGH

What happens to brown bears when they don't shave?

They turn into grizzly bears!

☐ LAUGH

Why are bulls so expensive?

Because they always CHARGE!

☐ LAUGH

What kind of coffee do fitness trainers order?

Pi-LATTES!

☐ LAUGH

Why do camels do so well in the desert?

Because they are CAMEL-flouged!

☐ LAUGH

Time to add up your points! →

SCORE BOARD

Add up each Jokester's laugh points for this round!

JOKESTER 1

$\dfrac{}{\text{Total}}$ 18

JOKESTER 2

$\dfrac{}{\text{Total}}$ 18

ROUND WINNER

ROUND 2

Why did the lighter stop working?

It got FIRED!

LAUGH

Why did the dumbbells break-up?

Things just weren't working out!

LAUGH

How did the outlet feel when he met a plug?

Shocked!

LAUGH

What kind of movies do campers like to watch?

Something in-tents!

LAUGH

How do you get trains to play music?

Use a Conductor!

☐ LAUGH

What happened when the doctor became ill?

He got a taste of his own medicine.

☐ LAUGH

Why did the actor walk so cautiously?

The director told him to break a leg!

☐ LAUGH

Why shouldn't you fall in love with a pastry chef?

They'll just DESSERT you!

☐ LAUGH

Pass the book to Jokester 2! →

Knock Knock.
Who's there?
iPhone.
iPhone, who?
iPhone and iPhone and you never
pick up, so I had to come over!

LAUGH

What do you call a pumpkin
that's about to fall?
Squash.

LAUGH

What do you call a peanut
with a lot of money?
A CASH-ew!

LAUGH

Why was the root undefeated?
Because it couldn't be BEET!

LAUGH

Why did the kettle need a vacation?

To blow off some steam!

☐ LAUGH

What should you do if you start to go bald?

Brush it off!

☐ LAUGH

How do you remove the sleeves from a shirt?

You try your VEST!

☐ LAUGH

How does the sun contribute money to charity?

☐ LAUGH

It attempts to RAYS money, every day!

Time to add up your points! →

19

SCORE BOARD

Add up each Jokester's laugh points for this round!

JOKESTER 1

$$\frac{/8}{\text{Total}}$$

JOKESTER 2

$$\frac{/8}{\text{Total}}$$

ROUND WINNER

ROUND
3

Why were the initials arrested?

They wouldn't name any names! LAUGH

What did the bucket say, when the dried up hose claimed he could fill him up?

"You're not FULLING anyone!" (Fooling) LAUGH

What bird is also a fruit?

A Kiwi! LAUGH

Why did the magazine shut down?

They had a lot of ISSUES! LAUGH

 **JOKESTER 1**

What do you call a room full of untrue books?

A LIE-brary.

LAUGH

What kind of art do you make in your sleep?

SNORE-agami.

LAUGH

How do you cool down a wig?

You use a hair conditioner!

LAUGH

What is a soldier's least favorite month?

March!

LAUGH

Pass the book to Jokester 2! ➔

What did the fruits say, when they finally stopped fighting?

"Let's BERRY this once and for all!"

LAUGH

Why did the judge wear a basketball jersey?

Because the ball was in his court!

LAUGH

What did the barbell say to cheer up his son?

"Don't worry son, I'm sure it'll WORK-OUT!"

LAUGH

What was the cause of the phone's bad break-up?

A bad connection.

LAUGH

What's the worst part about becoming an artist?

People assume that you're SKETCH-y.

☐ LAUGH

Why do travel agents hate the stairs?

They are always TRIP-ping!

 LAUGH

Why is a traffic light the best at recycling?

It loves going green!

☐ LAUGH

Why does the car never go anywhere?

It lacks MOTOR-vation!

 LAUGH

Time to add up your points! →

SCORE BOARD

Add up each Jokester's laugh points for this round!

JOKESTER 1

$\frac{18}{\text{Total}}$

JOKESTER 2

$\frac{18}{\text{Total}}$

ROUND WINNER

ROUND

4

Which part of a drumset is most like a trap?

The Snare.

LAUGH

Why are unicorns so bad at giving speeches?

They've only got one point!

LAUGH

What happened on the lighter's first date with the candle?

It just couldn't STRIKE UP a conversation.
I guess it wasn't a good MATCH!

LAUGH

How come the tree gives the best directions?

It always knows the best ROOT!

LAUGH

What did the baseball player say, before signing the contract?

"What's the CATCH?"

○ LAUGH

Why are tennis players considered bad neighbors?

They're always making a RACKET!

○ LAUGH

I'm improving my golf swing. I'm getting it down to a T.

○ LAUGH

What superhero likes to explore?

Wander Woman.

○ LAUGH

Pass the book to Jokester 2! →

29

What type of music do doctors listen to?

They're not picky, but something
with a good HEART-beat!

LAUGH

Why was the donut a good parent?

It was very HOLE-some!

LAUGH

I have a pet crow that talks to people for me.
I call it my-CROW-phone.

LAUGH

What did Maine say when America asked for a volunteer?

LAUGH

"ME!"

Why was the lightning told to change outfits?

It was too flashy!

LAUGH

What did the guy say when he won the city race?

"I RUN this town!"

LAUGH

Where's the best place to dance in the jungle?

Monkey Bars!

LAUGH

Why don't you have to invite rain over for a party?

It will just DROP in!

LAUGH

Time to add up your points! →

31

SCORE BOARD

Add up each Jokester's laugh points
for this round!

JOKESTER 1

$$\frac{\quad\quad}{\text{Total}} \quad /8$$

JOKESTER 2

$$\frac{\quad\quad}{\text{Total}} \quad /8$$

ROUND WINNER

ROUND 5

Why was the bull expelled from school?

His work wasn't credi-BULL!

 LAUGH

Why don't bears ride in elevators?

They're CLAWS-trophobic!

 LAUGH

Why was the soda so anxious?

He had so much bottled up!

 LAUGH

What do moths like best for breakfast?

COAT-meal.

 LAUGH

Why do you need a partner to make beef soup?

It takes stew!

☐ LAUGH

What did the egg say after finishing a simple test?

"Over! Easy."

☐ LAUGH

What do you call an actor who cares?

A CARE-acter!

☐ LAUGH

My grandmother gave me the mouthwash she's had in her closet for 50 years. Surprisingly, it's still in mint condition!

☐ LAUGH

Pass the book to Jokester 2! ➡

What did the baker say, when he went on break?

"I'll be back in dough time!"

LAUGH

What kind of sandwich is the most curious?

Anything on Wonderbread.

LAUGH

What do you call the bottom of a peppermint patty?

The base-MINT!

LAUGH

Why do math teachers hang out together?

Because there's strength in numbers!

LAUGH

What did the genie say as he granted the wish for a private island?

"ISLE be there."

 LAUGH

Why is credit better than cash?

It isn't TEAR-able!

LAUGH

What bird is self-motivated?

A Pel-I-can!

 LAUGH

Why do pigs have to work every day?

 LAUGH

Someone has to bring home the bacon!

Time to add up your points! →

SCORE BOARD

Add up each Jokester's laugh points for this round!

JOKESTER 1

$\dfrac{\quad/8\quad}{\text{Total}}$

JOKESTER 2

$\dfrac{\quad/8\quad}{\text{Total}}$

ROUND WINNER

ROUND

6

What did the orthodontist say to the patient?

"BRACE yourself!"

◯ LAUGH

Why did the music composer have to pull over on the side of the road?

He saw he had to change 'A Flat'!

◯ LAUGH

Teacher: "Jimmy, use the word 'butter' in a sentence." Jimmy: "The wind blew on the girl, butter hat stayed on!"

◯ LAUGH

Why did the car give up the race?

He needed more DRIVE!

◯ LAUGH

JOKESTER 1

What happens to a T-Rex after it works out?

It gets dino-SORE!

☐ LAUGH

What part of the car was designed by cows?

The STEER-ing wheel!

☐ LAUGH

What can you say to make newborn pups stay quiet?

"Hush, puppies!"

☐ LAUGH

Why were the trees so excited for the football game?

They wanted to ROOT for their team!

☐ LAUGH

Pass the book to Jokester 2! →

The yoga teacher is such a hard worker. She's always bending over backwards to get things done!

LAUGH

Why couldn't the pirate make any friends?

He would always ARRGH-ue!

LAUGH

Why didn't the Egyptian man want to get out of the river?

Well, between you and I, he was stuck in de-NILE.

LAUGH

What do you call a peppermint flying through outer space?

COMET-mint!

LAUGH

What instrument has the best grin?
The Smile-in!

LAUGH

What kind of art do athletes like?
ABS-tract!

LAUGH

How do you know if the bell tower isn't working?
It won't ring on chime!

LAUGH

Why wasn't the runner eating?
He was on a FAST!

LAUGH

Time to add up your points! ➡

SCORE BOARD

Add up each Jokester's laugh points
for this round!

JOKESTER 1

$$\frac{/8}{\text{Total}}$$

JOKESTER 2

$$\frac{/8}{\text{Total}}$$

ROUND WINNER

ROUND

7

What season is best for practicing addition?

SUM-mer!

LAUGH

The puppy thought he'd have no fun at the dog park without a toy to play with, but he ended up having a ball!

LAUG.

How did the sword fighter keep people off her lawn?

Fencing!

LAUGH

Why does sewing machine thread smell so bad?

It lives in the SEW-er.

LAUG

Which two states love Elvis?

The Rock and Ca-ROLL-ina's!

☐ LAUGH

What do you call indecisive shoes?

Flip flops.

☐ LAUGH

Do geologists like learning about rocks?

Of Quartz, they do!

☐ LAUGH

Did you hear about the man who dropped his glass?

It's breaking news!

☐ LAUGH

Pass the book to Jokester 2! →

Why did the pianist switch to the organ?

He heard going 100% ORGAN-ic was healthier!

LAUGH

What's the rapper's favorite type of chocolate?

M&M.

LAUGH

What did the corn say to the farmer?

"Stop stalking me!"

LAUGH

Why did the fire fall in love with the log?

He found a good match!

 LAUGH

What made the Lion King a bad leader?

He let his PRIDE get the best of him.

☐ LAUGH

What do you get when you cross a cat and a cactus?

A PLANT-a-pus!

☐ LAUGH

What kind of coffee do baby cows like?

De-CALF-inated.

☐ LAUGH

What do rats do before buying a new car?

They take it on a pest drive!

☐ LAUGH

Time to add up your points! ➙

49

SCORE BOARD

Add up each Jokester's laugh points for this round!

JOKESTER 1

$$\frac{/8}{\text{Total}}$$

JOKESTER 2

$$\frac{/8}{\text{Total}}$$

ROUND WINNER

ROUND

8

 **JOKESTER 1**

What did the elevator tell the stairs as it was going up?

"Get on my level!"

LAUGH

Why didn't the tuba ever fall over?

It had a strong bass!

LAUGH

What do you call it when you can't catch any fish?

Fishin' Impossible.

LAUGH

What happened when Dr. Frankenstein removed the monster's brain?

LAUG

Not sure, they said it was a no-brainer!

What did the dry grass say?

"WATER you waiting for?!"

☐ LAUGH

What key on the computer allows you to get an alien drink?

The Space Bar!

☐ LAUGH

What do you call a junkyard on an asteroid?

A Waste of Space.

☐ LAUGH

Why did the quarterback refuse help?

He always PASSES!

☐ LAUGH

Pass the book to Jokester 2! ➔

What do you call woods where you can sleep?

For-REST.

LAUGH

Why was the plus sign feeling so positive?

It just saw an inspirational add!

LAUGH

What did the worker plant ask his boss, the Sun, for?

A Rays! (Raise)

LAUGH

Knock Knock.
Who's there?
Vonnie.
Vonnie, who?
Vonnie you should ask! It's me!

LAUG

 **JOKESTER 2**

How does a mountain give a recap?

They SUMMIT all up!

☐ LAUGH

How do you know if you should go to the doctor for the flu?

A gut feeling...

☐ LAUGH

Which school dance did the geometry teacher chaperone?

The Square Dance.

☐ LAUGH

Why was the bison hiding? ☐ LAUGH

It wanted to keep a buffa-LOW PROFILE!

Time to add up your points! ➡

SCORE BOARD

Add up each Jokester's laugh points for this round!

JOKESTER 1

$$\frac{}{\text{Total}} \, /8$$

JOKESTER 2

$$\frac{}{\text{Total}} \, /8$$

ROUND WINNER

ROUND

9

What did one foot say to the other, after they won the dance contest?

"I TOE-d you! We were a shoe-in to win!"

LAUGH

How do you propose to someone in a grocery store?

Tell them, "AISLE always love you!"

LAUGH

What is the best season to gift someone a slinky?

Spring!

LAUGH

The book got a new house. He's starting a new CHAPTER in his life.

LAUGH

Where does candy stay while on vacation?

In a suite, of course!

LAUGH ☐

What do you call a forest full of jungle cats?

Tiger Woods!

LAUGH ☐

What do you get when you cross a pineapple, watermelon, grapes, and a pterodactyl?

A healthy in-flight snack!

LAUGH ☐

Why did the wrestler compete against his fiancé?

He wanted to share a RING with her!

LAUGH ☐

Pass the book to Jokester 2! ➝

How does a tortoise go
40 miles an hour?

Uber!

LAUGH

Why did the doe go
to the bank?

She wanted to borrow a few BUCKS!

LAUGH

What pasta is only worth
one cent?

Penne.

LAUGH

A judge has ruled that all public
schools must have at least
1/4 a gymnasium. It's a
court-ordered quarter court!

LAUGH

Why doesn't paper understand shredders?

It finds them puzzling.

☐ LAUGH

My brother and I agree we're both the same height. I'm glad we see eye to eye.

☐ LAUGH

How do you explore the woods, without a map?

Trail and error.

☐ LAUGH

The short man didn't understand any of the jokes. They all went over his head!

☐ LAUGH

Time to add up your points! →

SCORE BOARD

Add up each Jokester's laugh points for this round!

JOKESTER 1

$$\frac{/8}{\text{Total}}$$

JOKESTER 2

$$\frac{/8}{\text{Total}}$$

ROUND WINNER

ROUND

10

What makes clocks so generous?

They have two helping hands and are always willing to give you the time of day!

LAUGH

How can you tell when a bucket is worn out?

It starts to look rather PALE.

LAUGH

What did the tailor say, right before he got fired?

"If you want to fire me, SUIT yourself!"

LAUGH

What does a copying machine and a good cop have in common?

They both know how to keep the fax straight.

LAUGH

Why did the penguin get off the ride?

He had cold feet.

LAUGH ☐

Why is the zebra always working so hard?

He has to earn his stripes!

LAUGH ☐

Did you know I was near a gas explosion once?

I almost had a fart attack!

LAUGH ☐

Why was the shredded cheese in such a good mood?

It had been feeling GRATE all day!

LAUGH ☐

Pass the book to Jokester 2! ➝

What did the baker say, before she invented the first pretzel?

"Why knot?"

⬭ LAUGH

How do ghosts save money on paper?

They only use one sheet!

⬭ LAUGH

What do snipers like to do in their spare time?

SHOOT the breeze.

⬭ LAUGH

Did you know that cornfields are actually great listeners?

That's because they're all EARS!

⬭ LAUGH

Why did the phone go to the doctor?

It needed a screen-SHOT.

LAUGH ☐

What kind of make-up will help you study?

The highlighter!

LAUGH ☐

Knock Knock.
Who's there?
Zatta-tatt.
Zatta-tatt, who?
No, it's a birthmark.

LAUGH ☐

What does Bugs Bunny say when he parks his boat?

LAUGH ☐

"What's up, Dock?"

Time to add up your points! →

SCORE BOARD

Add up each Jokester's laugh points for this round!

JOKESTER 1

$\dfrac{}{\text{Total}}$ /8

JOKESTER 2

$\dfrac{}{\text{Total}}$ /8

ROUND WINNER

Add up all your points from each round.
The Jokester with the most points is crowned

The Laugh Master!

In the event of a tie, continue to Round 11
- The Tie-Breaker Round!

JOKESTER 1

_____
Grand Total

JOKESTER 2

_____
Grand Total

_____
THE LAUGH MASTER

ROUND

11

TIE-BREAKER
(Winner Takes ALL!)

What is a basketball shoe's favorite type of music?
Sole!

LAUGH

What part of a church is always changing?
The Alter!

LAUGH

Knock Knock.
Who's there?
Day Jav.
Day Jav, who?
I feel like this has happened before...

LAUGH

What rodent is the most religious?
A Chip-MONK.

LAUGH

What do you call a naked fish?

A BARE-acuda.

☐ LAUGH

What brand of diaper does Cupid wear?

Luvs.

☐ LAUGH

What kind of car does a kitten drive?

A CAT-illac.

☐ LAUGH

A pirate got in a sword fight and came back to work the next day wearing a patch. When his boss asked what happened, all he could say was, "Eye, Captain".

☐ LAUGH

Pass the book to Jokester 2! ➜

Why does the boxer enjoy fishing so much?

Because he loves a good HOOK!

LAUGH

What do you call a stick man with no head, arms or legs?

Mark!

LAUGH

Why was the cow angry with the farmer?

He'd milked her for all she was worth!

LAUGH

What did the barn say to the door?

"Our opening totally HINGES on you!"

LAUGH

The ink is so happy to be set free. He just spent ten years in the pen.

☐ LAUGH

What do you say, when there is a lot of sand near the ocean?

"To beach their own!"

☐ LAUGH

What do you call a broadcast of a kettle heating up on a stove?

Live-steaming!

☐ LAUGH

Did you hear about the shoe salesman, who got fired?

They said he got the boot!

☐ LAUGH

Time to add up your points! →

Add up all your points from the
Tie-Breaker Round.
The Jokester with the most points is crowned

The Laugh Master!

JOKESTER 1   /8
                Total

JOKESTER 2   /8
                Total

_____

THE LAUGH MASTER

Check out our

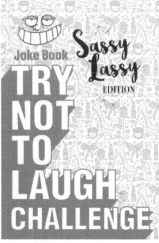

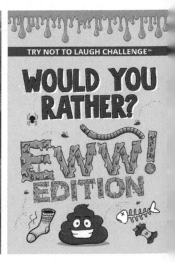

Visit our Amazon Store at:

other joke books!

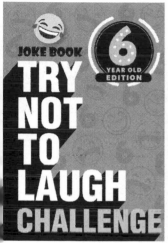

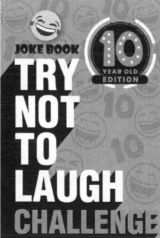
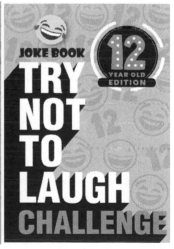

www.Amazon.com/author/CrazyCorey

Made in the USA
San Bernardino, CA
17 November 2019